1001
Things to Spot
in the Sea

Katie Daynes

Illustrated by Teri Gower

Designed by Natacha Goransky

Edited by Anna Milbourne

Natural history consultant: Dr. Margaret Rostron

SCHOLASTIC INC.

New York Toronto London Auckland Sydney
Mexico City New Delhi Hong Kong Buenos Aires

Contents

Things to spot

The scenes in this book show seas and oceans from around the world. In each scene there are lots of things for you to find and count.

There is also a puzzle on pages 30 to 31 with even more things to spot in the sea. There are 1001 things for you to spot altogether.

Underwater forest

10 garibaldi fish

8 turban snails

5 black rock fish

9 kelp crabs

8 kelp bass

4 sea otters

10 sea urchins

6 sea fans

2 leopard sharks

9 kelp fish

Each little picture shows you what to look for in the big picture.

The blue number tells you how many of that thing you need to find.

This is Billy. He has explored seas and oceans all over the world. He always takes his underwater camera with him. As you go through the book, see if you can spot Billy's camera in each scene.

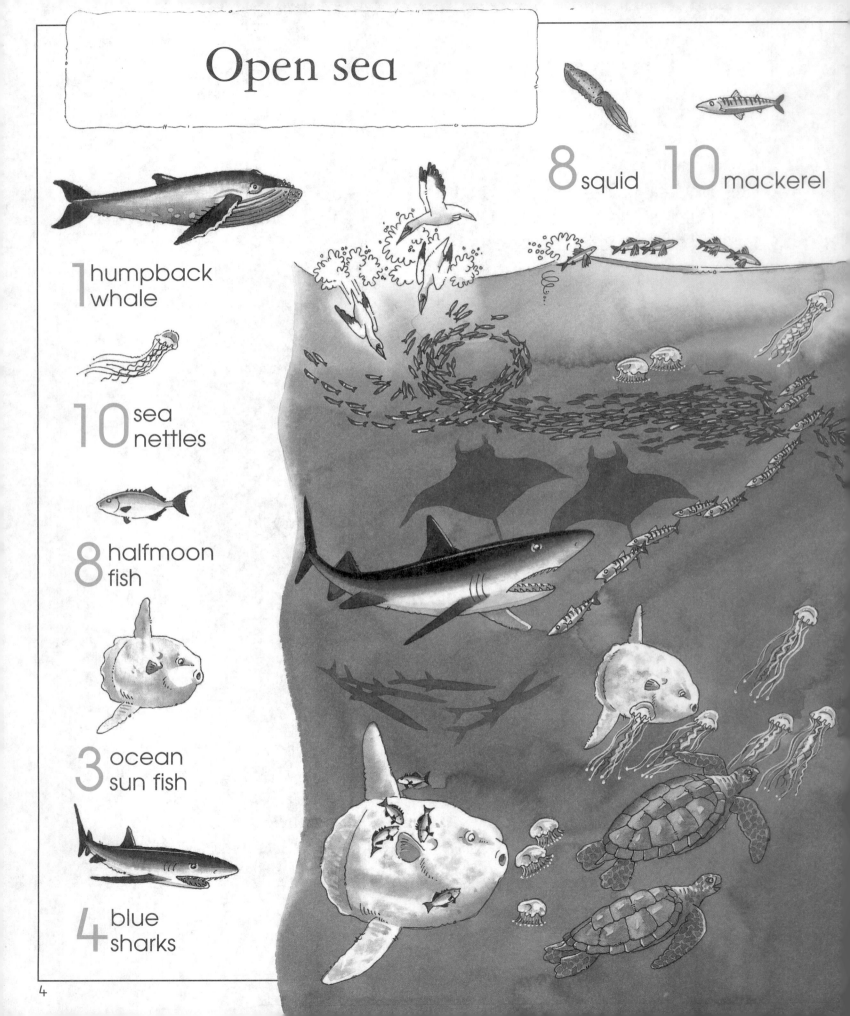

Open sea

8 squid   **10** mackerel

1 humpback whale

10 sea nettles

8 halfmoon fish

3 ocean sun fish

4 blue sharks

9 flying fish

7 little tunnies

3 gannets

Water sports

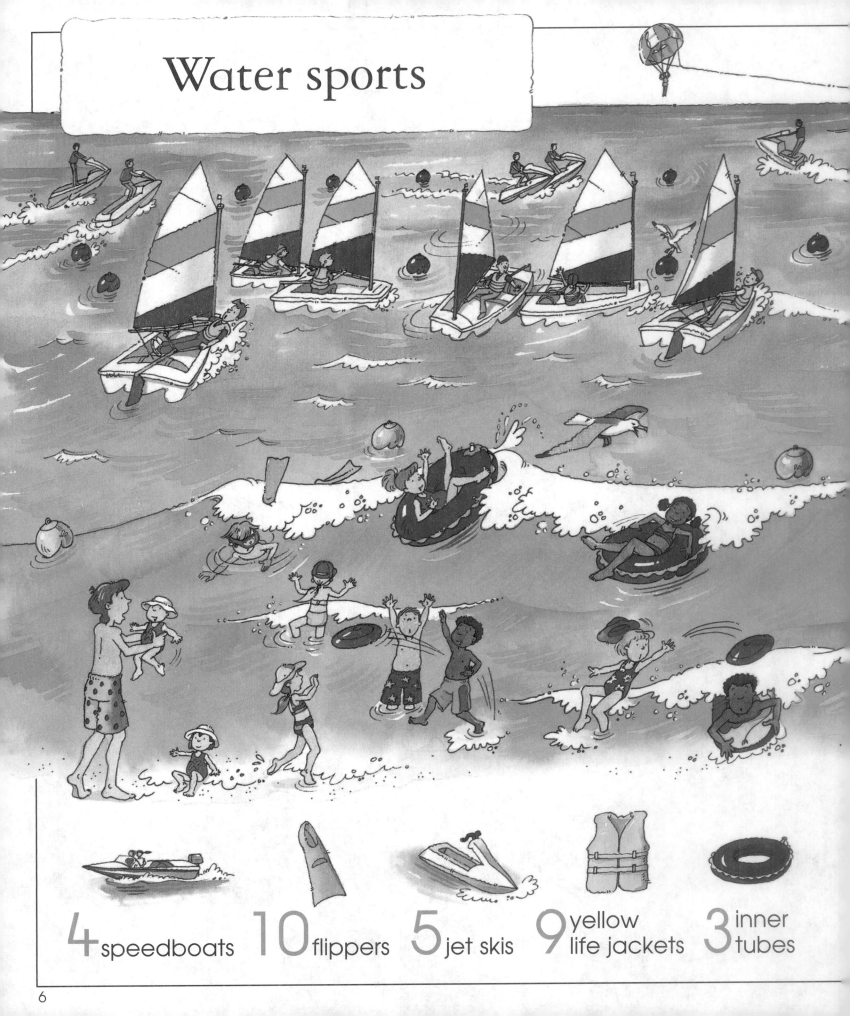

4 speedboats   10 flippers   5 jet skis   9 yellow life jackets   3 inner tubes

9 red buoys   6 striped sails   10 herring gulls   5 windsurfers   7 boogie boards

Icy north

10 harp seals

8 seal pups

10 capelin

4 arctic terns

8 ringed seals

4 polar bears

9 arctic cod

5 white parkas

3 killer whales

9 arctic charr

Coral reef

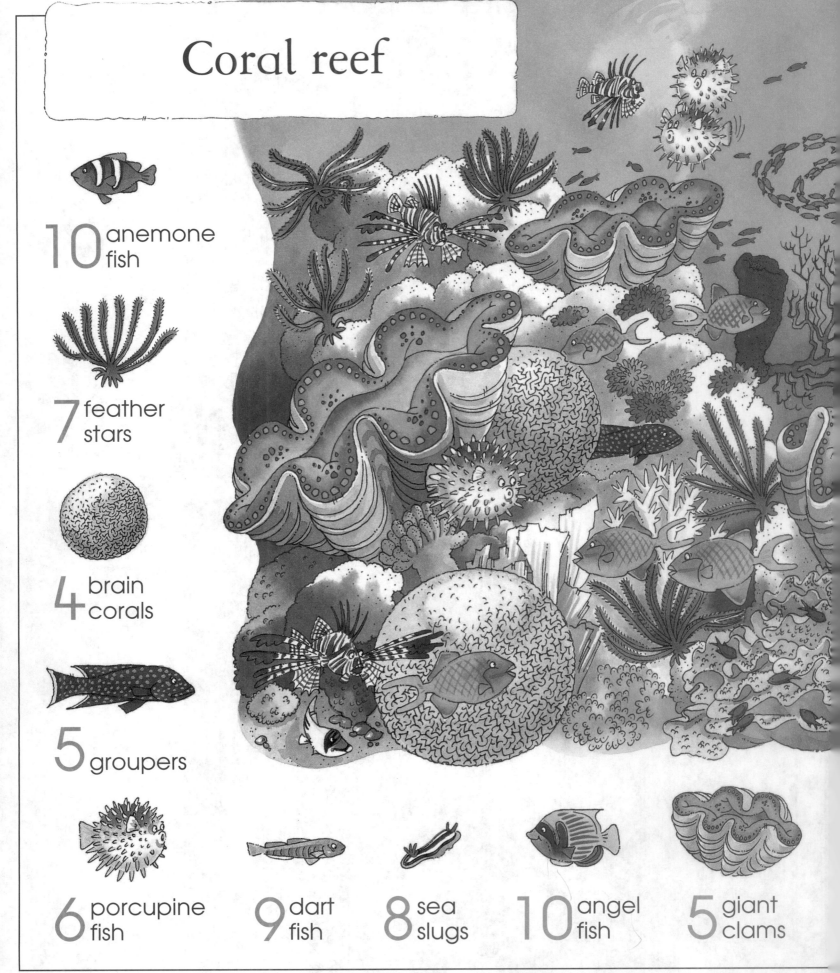

10 anemone fish

7 feather stars

4 brain corals

5 groupers

6 porcupine fish

9 dart fish

8 sea slugs

10 angel fish

5 giant clams

9 trigger fish

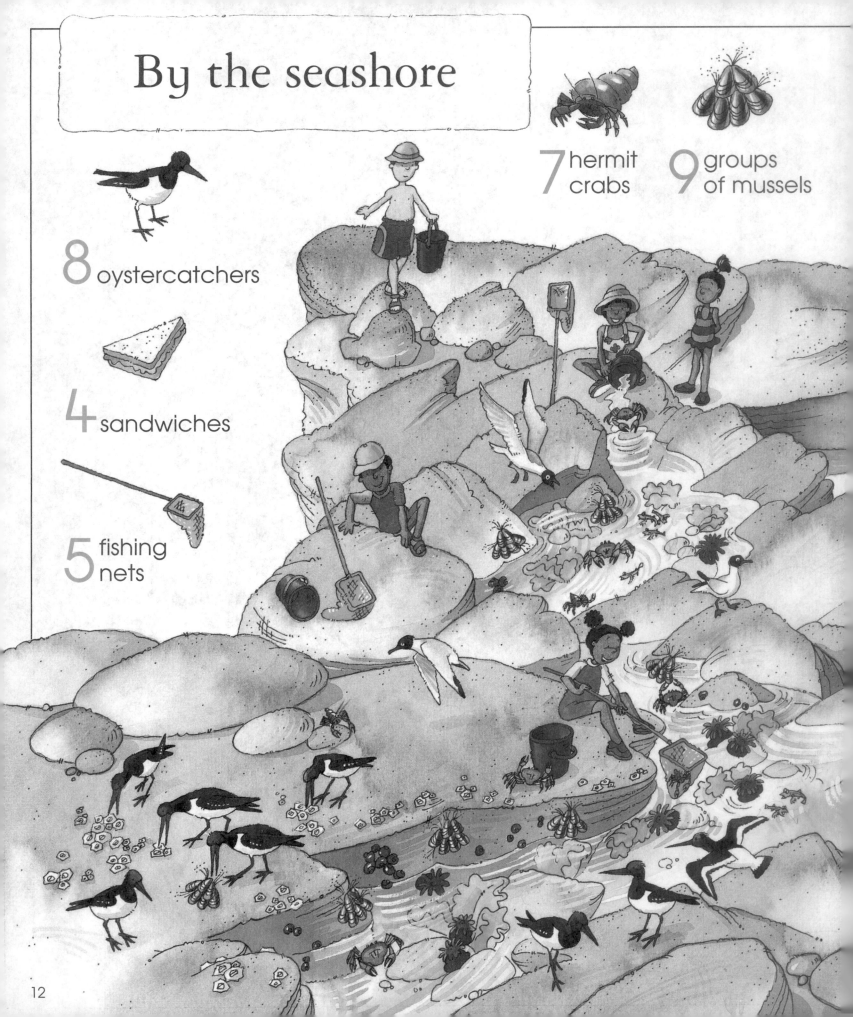

By the seashore

8 oystercatchers

4 sandwiches

5 fishing nets

7 hermit crabs

9 groups of mussels

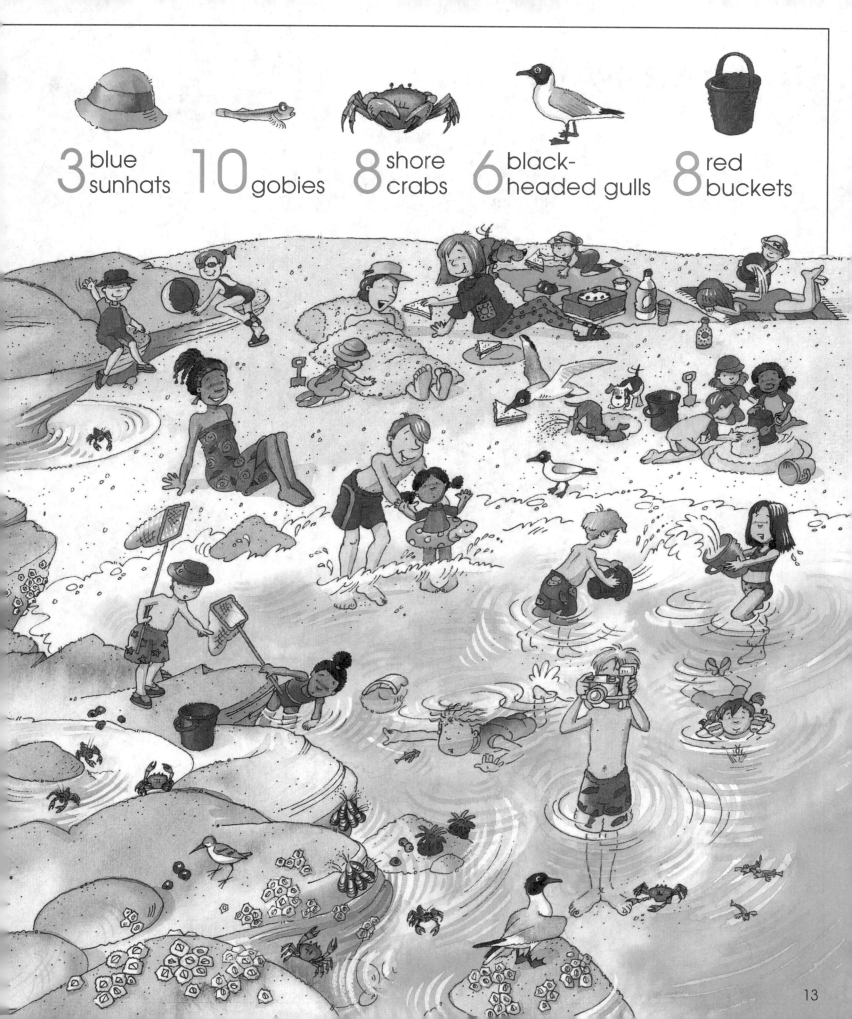

3 blue sunhats
10 gobies
8 shore crabs
6 black-headed gulls
8 red buckets

Underwater forest

10 garibaldi fish

8 turban snails

5 black rock fish

9 kelp crabs

8 kelp bass

4 sea otters

10 sea urchins

6 sea fans

2 leopard sharks

9 kelp fish

On a cruise

3 lifeboats

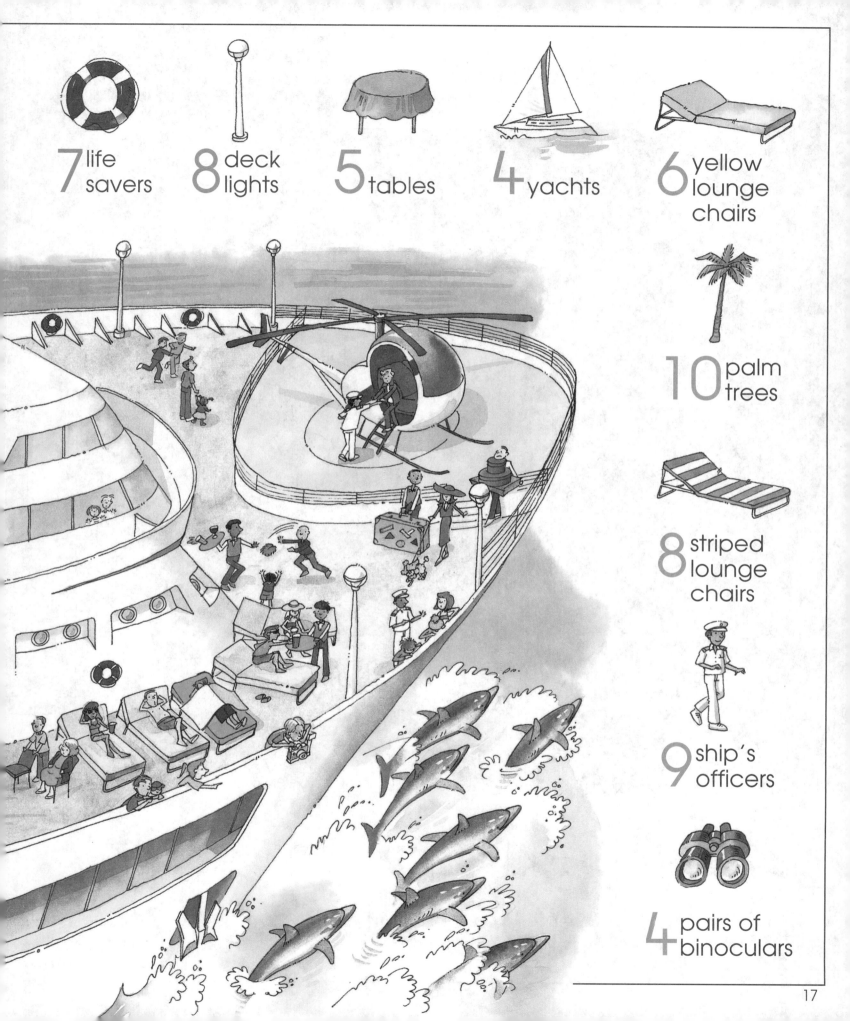

7 life savers

8 deck lights

5 tables

4 yachts

6 yellow lounge chairs

10 palm trees

8 striped lounge chairs

9 ship's officers

4 pairs of binoculars

Deep down

10 lantern fish

9 vent shrimps

8 spook fish

10 vent crabs

7 black smokers

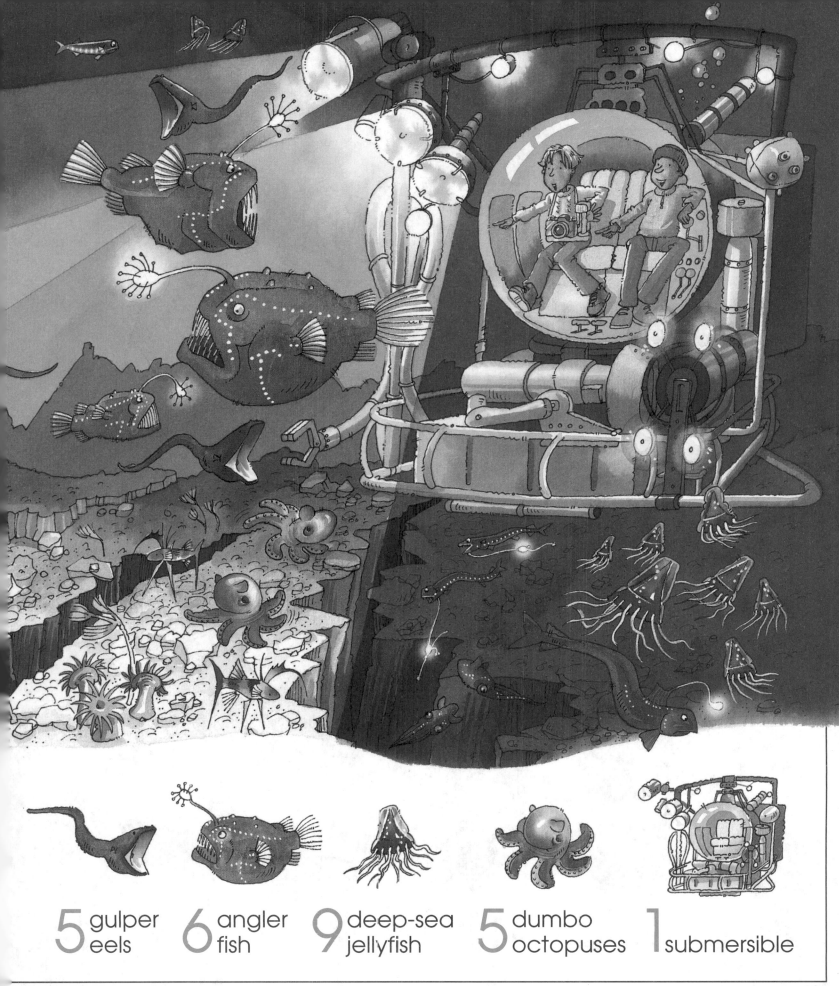

5 gulper eels   6 angler fish   9 deep-sea jellyfish   5 dumbo octopuses   1 submersible

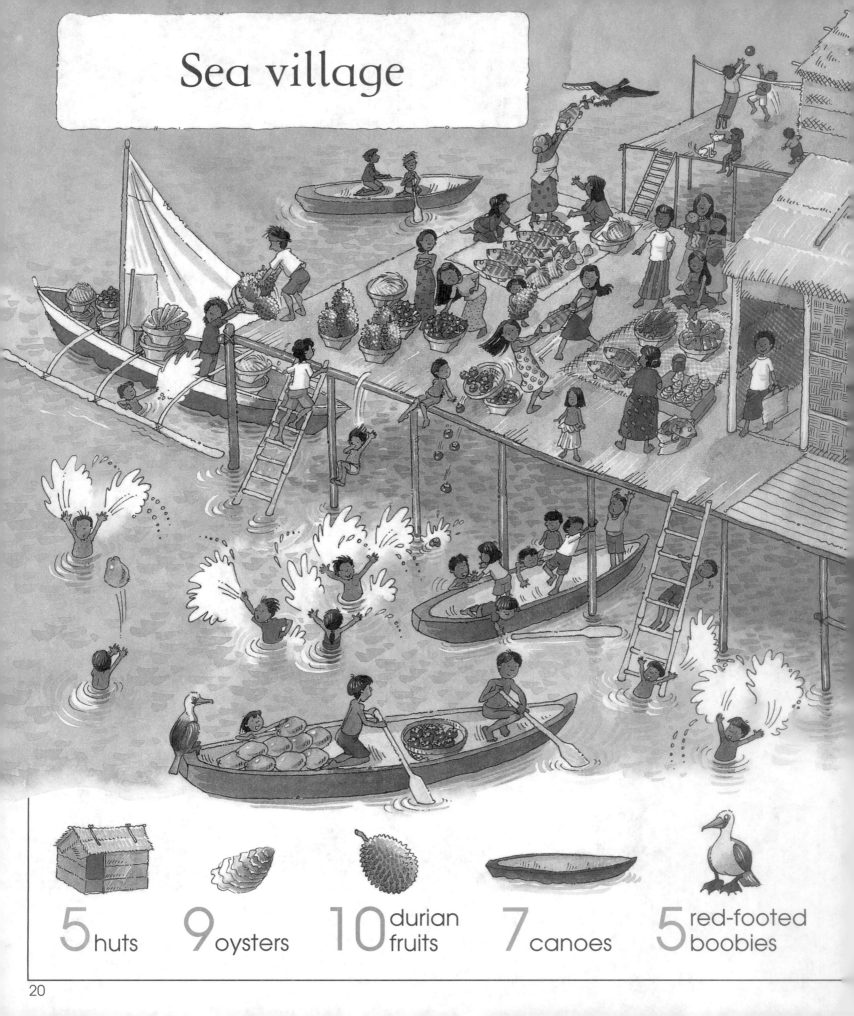

Sea village

5 huts   9 oysters   10 durian fruits   7 canoes   5 red-footed boobies

10 paddles   **8** white T-shirts   **10** coconuts   **6** ladders   **4** dogs

Lost city

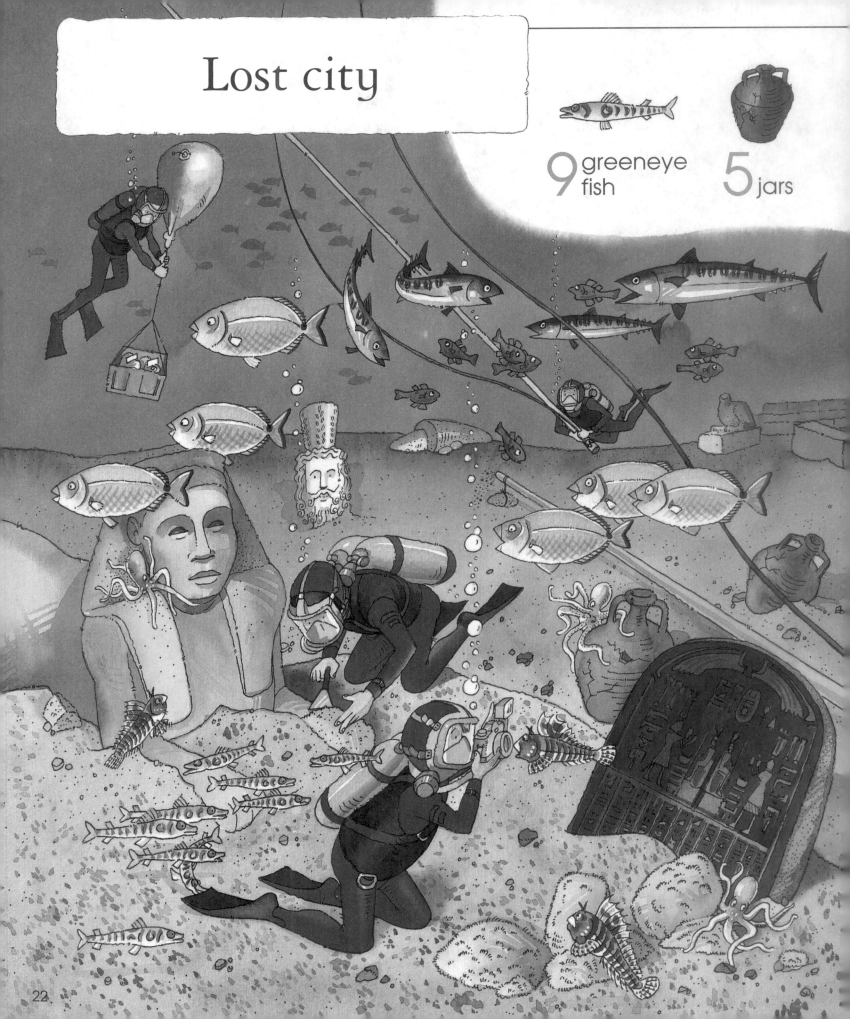

9 greeneye fish

5 jars

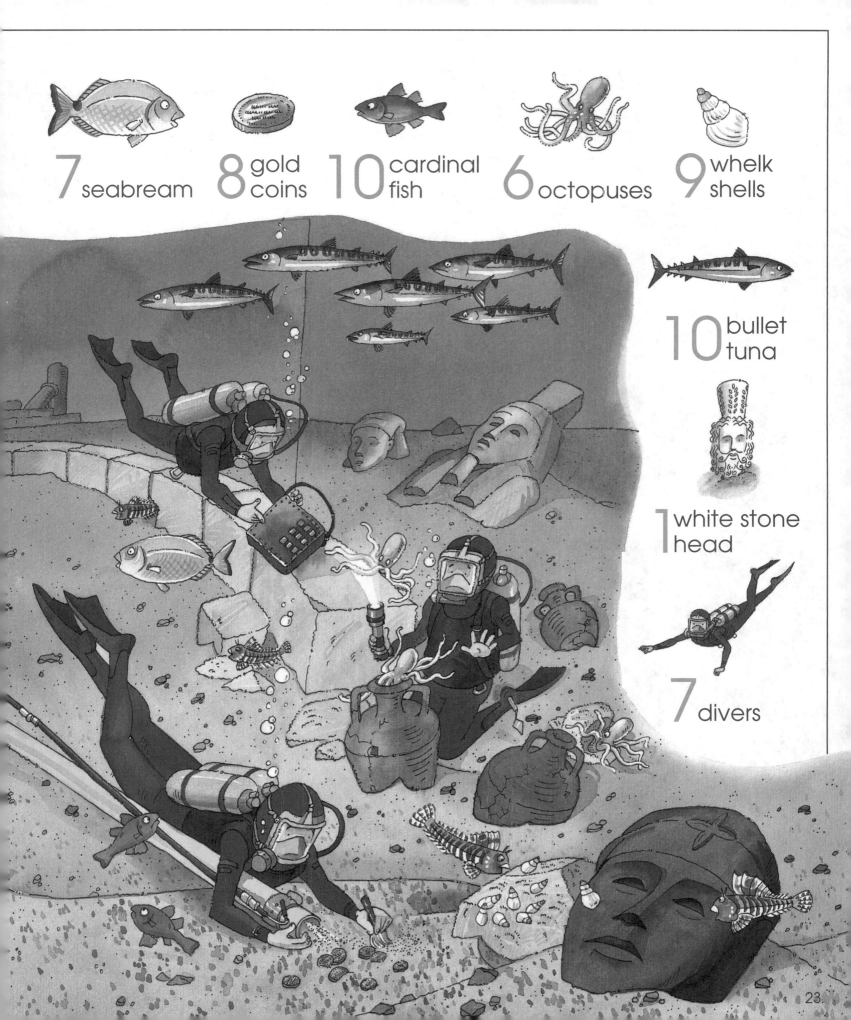

7 seabream

8 gold coins

10 cardinal fish

6 octopuses

9 whelk shells

10 bullet tuna

1 white stone head

7 divers

Chilly south

9 chinstrap penguins **8** albatrosses

1 whale-watchers' tour boat

5 elephant seals

3 whale tails

6 backpacks

10 king penguins

10 penguin chicks

9 brown skuas

4 hourglass dolphins

Grassy seabed

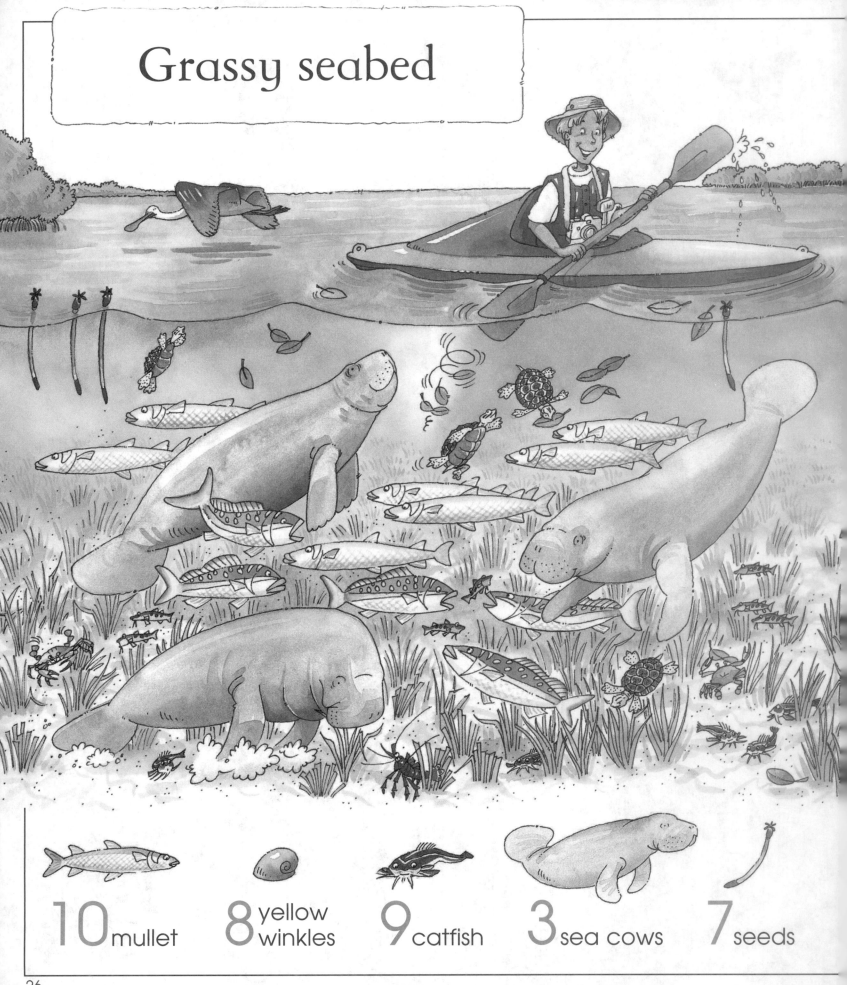

10 mullet 8 yellow winkles 9 catfish 3 sea cows 7 seeds

9 snappers

5 roseate spoonbills

8 blue crabs

7 terrapins

10 butterfly fish

Shipwreck

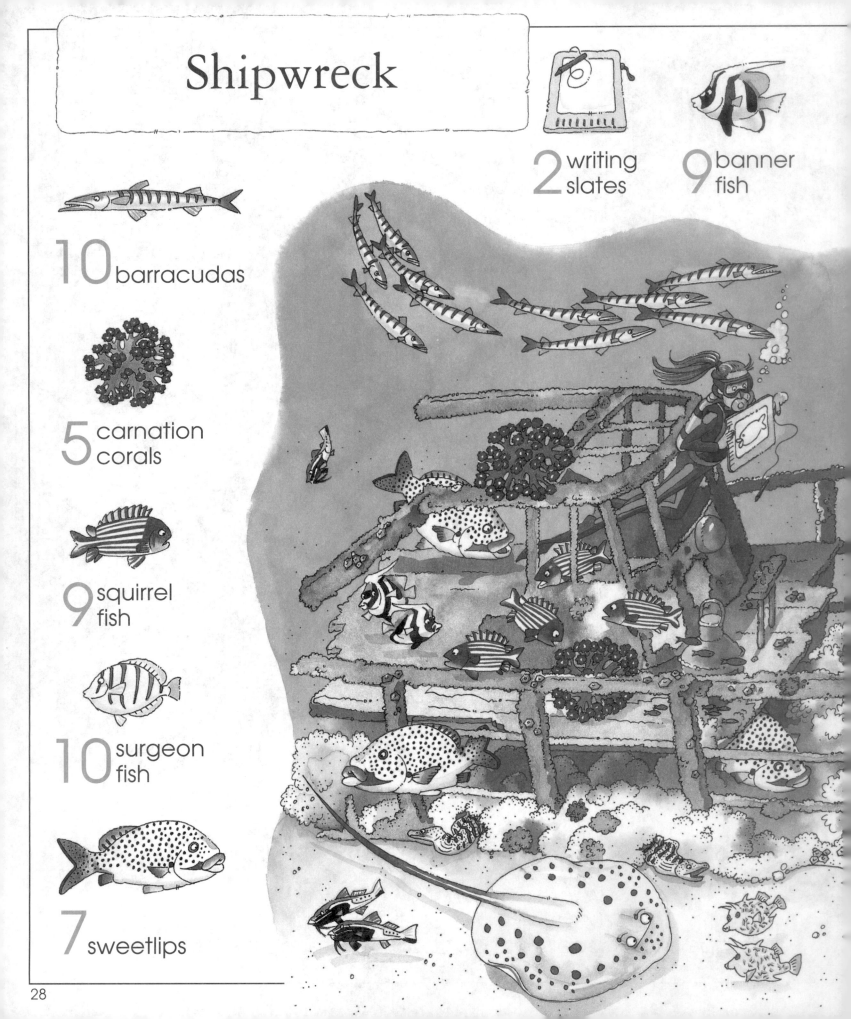

2 writing slates

9 banner fish

10 barracudas

5 carnation corals

9 squirrel fish

10 surgeon fish

7 sweetlips

4 moray eels

1 anchor

8 cow fish

At the aquarium

Aquariums help you find out about sea animals. This aquarium shows animals from this book. Can you find which scenes they are from and count them all?

7 moon jellyfish

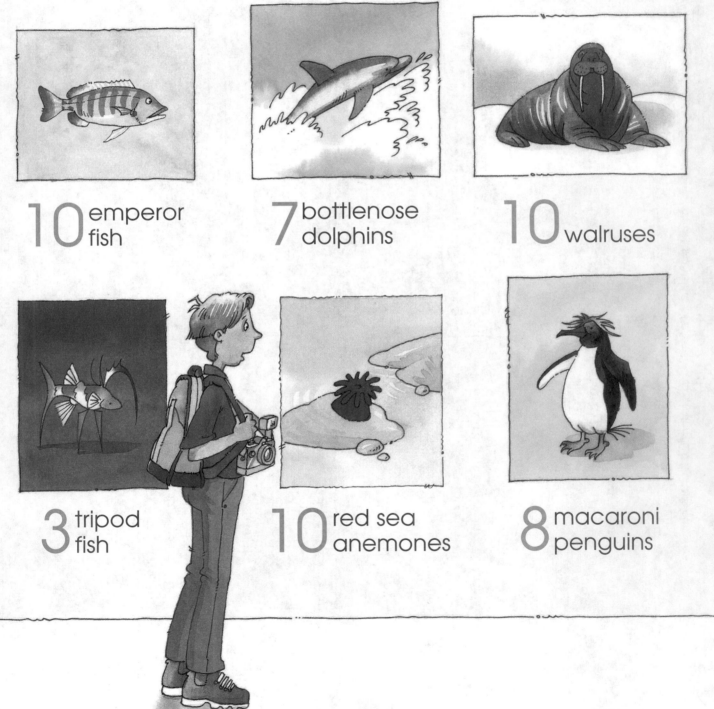

10 emperor fish

7 bottlenose dolphins

10 walruses

3 tripod fish

10 red sea anemones

8 macaroni penguins

1 blue-spotted ray

2 napoleon wrasses

3 loggerhead turtles

8 seahorses

9 picasso fish

6 lion fish

6 spiny lobsters

7 butterfly blennies

5 sun stars

Answers

Did you find all the aquarium animals in the book? Here's where they are.

Posters of animals

7 moon jellyfish:
Open sea
(pages 4 and 5)

10 emperor fish:
Sea village
(pages 20 and 21)

7 bottlenose dolphins:
On a cruise
(pages 16 and 17)

10 walruses:
Icy north
(pages 8 and 9)

3 tripod fish:
Deep down
(pages 18 and 19)

10 red sea anemones:
By the seashore
(pages 12 and 13)

8 macaroni penguins:
Chilly south
(pages 24 and 25)

Animals in tanks

1 blue-spotted ray:
Shipwreck
(pages 28 and 29)

3 loggerhead turtles:
Open sea
(pages 4 and 5)

2 napoleon wrasses:
Shipwreck
(pages 28 and 29)

8 seahorses:
Grassy seabed
(pages 26 and 27)

9 picasso fish:
Coral reef
(pages 10 and 11)

6 lion fish:
Coral reef
(pages 10 and 11)

6 spiny lobsters:
Grassy seabed
(pages 26 and 27)

7 butterfly blennies:
Lost city
(pages 22 and 23)

5 sun stars:
Underwater forest
(pages 14 and 15)

Managing editor: Gillian Doherty
Managing designers: Mary Cartwright and Russell Punter

The publishers would like to thank the following people for their advice:
- Emad Khalil, underwater archaeologist at Southampton University
- Jonathan Mendez, chief powerboat instructor for the Royal Yachting Association
- Rachael Saul from Hebridean Island Cruises Ltd
- Matt Slater, marine biologist at Blue Reef Aquarium, Newquay
- Sally Thomas from The Royal Institute of Naval Architects